Flute
Grades 1-2

JAZZ CLUB

Piano Accompaniment
Contents

Series Editor: Sadie Cook
Production Editor: Anna Joyce
Music Engraving & CD Production: Artemis Music Limited
Recorded by: Jeff Leach (piano)
Cover Design: Dominic Brookman

Published 2001

All titles © 2001 International Music Publications Limited

JAZZ CLUB

Flute
Grades 1-2

DON'T BE
A MUSIC
COPYCAT!

The copying of © copyright
material is a criminal offence
and may lead to prosecution.

Reproducing this music in any form is illegal and forbidden
by the **Copyright, Designs and Patents Act 1988**

IMP

International
MUSIC
Publications

© International Music Publications Limited
Griffin House 161 Hammersmith Road London W6 8BS England

Introduction

Welcome to **Jazz Club**

This book contains ten pieces (two unaccompanied) that have been written to reflect the diverse **jazz** styles used by professional **jazz** musicians over the past fifty years or so. Each piece has been written specifically for the **flute** making best use of the range, **timbre** and agility of the instrument. The pieces become gradually more difficult as you make your way through the book. A short paragraph outlining tips on **rhythm, swing and articulation** for each piece is included in the instrumental insert, together with a listening recommendation.

In this first book, the difficulty lies mostly with interpreting **jazz rhythms, ties, pushed beats, swing** etc, however the range of notes required should present few problems. The piano accompaniments, featured on the CD, are designed to provide a strong rhythmic and harmonic background and although at first some may look a little tricky, a pianist of modest ability will find them playable with a small amount of practice.

Virtually every **jazz** musician has developed individuality of style by listening to other musicians and their recordings. It is strongly recommended that any **jazz** study-programme should include listening to **jazz** recordings – in particular compare the tones achieved by different performers and the way they apply varying degrees of swing.

Enjoy this book and let it be the start of a lifelong affinity with **jazz**.

Road hog

Quick and funky

Dawn chorus

Fairly slow, with feeling

Bombay blues

Slow blues tempo

free tempo (even quavers)

Waltz for
those without

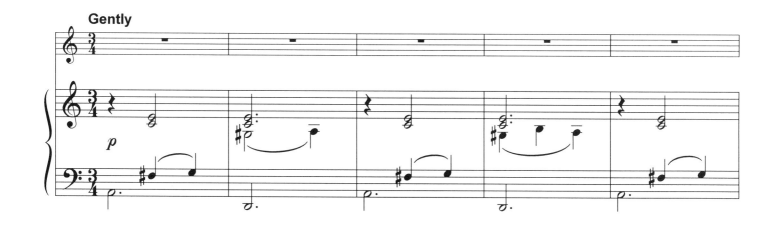

Jazz Club

Flute
Grades 1-2

Contents

Series Editor: Sadie Cook
Production Editor: Anna Joyce
Music Engraving & CD Production: Artemis Music Limited
Recorded by: Jeff Leach (piano)
Cover Design: Dominic Brookman

Published 2001
All titles © 2001 International Music Publications Limited

Reproducing this music in any form
is illegal and forbidden by the
Copyright, Designs and Patents Act 1988

International MUSIC Publications
© International Music Publications Limited
Griffin House 161 Hammersmith Road London W6 8BS England

2

Road hog

This piece is written in a **funk** style. Play with **even quavers** and follow the staccato and tenuto markings for the right **effect**. **Jeremy Steig** is a rock, jazz and funk flautist who achieves a special effect by **singing** and playing at the same time.

Quick and funky

Dawn chorus

Slow jazz pieces like this are known as **ballads**. The quavers are not swung, and there is room for much **expression**. Keep the long **phrases** going to test your breath control. **Hubert Lawes** is a jazz flautist with immense **control** over his playing in a variety of modern styles, including ballads.

Fairly slow, with feeling

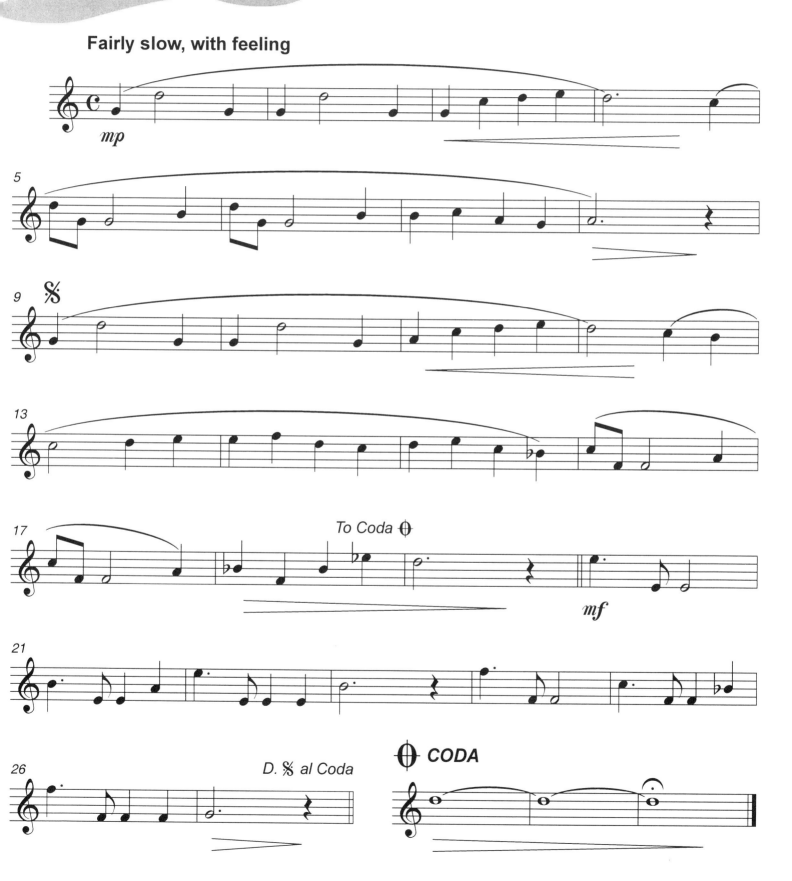

Bombay blues

This is a simple **12-bar blues** with a short **cadenza** at the end. Swing the quavers gently up to the cadenza, from then on make sure the quavers are even but in a **rubato** tempo. **James Moody**, mostly known as a saxophonist but also a fine flautist, was an expert at slow blues playing.

Slow blues tempo

free tempo (even quavers)

Soul statement

Try playing around with the **tempo** in this piece. Make the **rests** last much longer than their actual value. Speed up in bars 10 and 11, otherwise make the music last as **long** as you can. This piece is inspired by trumpeter **Miles Davis'** playing of 'Prayer' from his album '**Porgy And Bess**'.

Slow rubato with even quavers

Waltz for those without

There is no need to swing anything here as it might make the music sound sticky.
A **simple approach** is best for this piece, which is inspired by pianist **Bill Evans'**
'Waltz For Debby'. Watch out for the long trills – keep them sustained and even.

Ant behaviour

An odd piece with an odd title, this is based on the **diminished** scale (alternating tones and semitones). **Quavers** should not be swung, and you could perhaps slow down a touch from bar 13. Although the **harmony** is jazz-based, this could be a **classical** piece. Listen to any great flautist to hear how **rich** the tone of the instrument can be.

Ant tempo

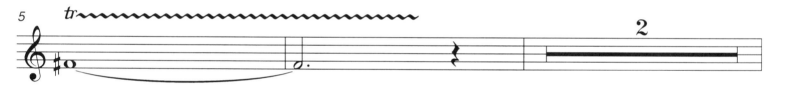

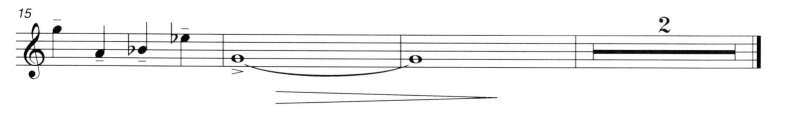

Orbiting venus

Use a fairly quick **swing** tempo for this piece. Follow the **slurs** and keep the longer notes going for their full **value**. This piece is unaccompanied, so be careful not to lose momentum. **Roland Kirk** (who was famous for playing three saxophones at once) was a fine modern jazz flautist who might have played music in this style.

Bad hair day

This piece is in the **West Coast** jazz style. Don't **articulate** the staccato notes too harshly, just make sure they are detached. **Broaden** the tone for the middle section of the piece (bars 19 to 26). Many West Coast big bands, such as **Shorty Rogers** and **Marty Paich**, featured flutes in their compositions.

Steady swing

Mango number 5

A **Mambo** is a Cuban **dance** rhythm in which quavers are played **evenly**. Follow the **articulation** exactly and never rush or you will be out of time with the piano. Even though the piece looks very long there is a lot of **repetition**, so don't be put off. Listen to **Herbie Mann** for recordings of Latin American flute playing.

Steady Mambo

Southern fried

A light **jazz-rock** feel is required here. Even quavers, with very little slurring and the occasional **staccato**, are sufficient for the character of the piece. Be careful with the **tempo** during any break in the accompaniment. **The Cannonball Adderley Sextet**, which often played this **soul** style of music, featured **Charles Lloyd** playing both flute and tenor sax.

Moderately, with even quavers

Ant behaviour

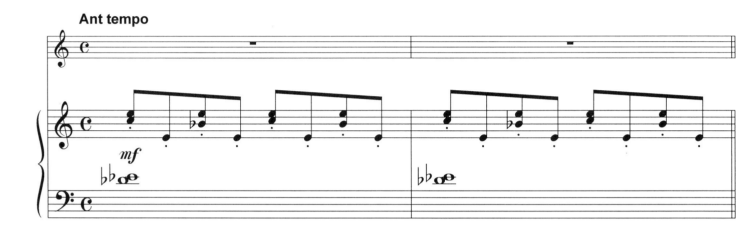

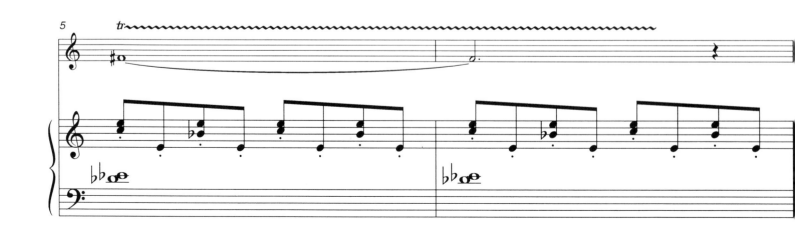

Bad hair day

Steady swing

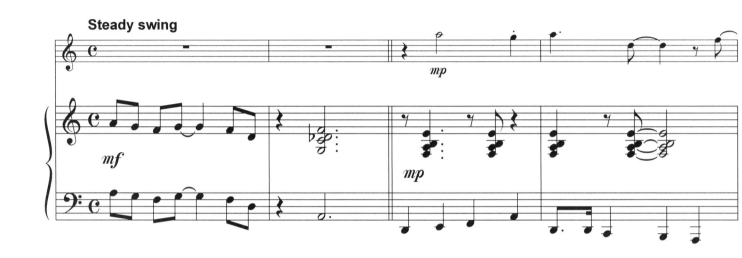

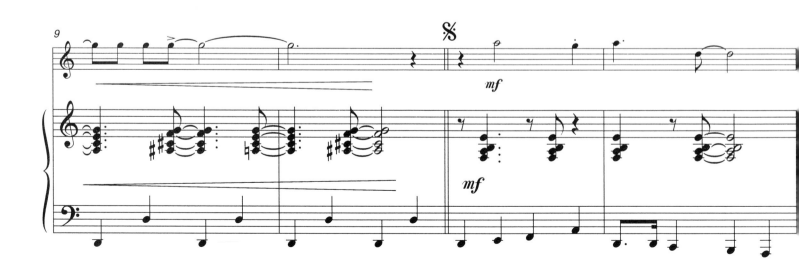

Mango number 5

Steady Mambo

Southern fried

Moderately, with even quavers